ISOLATORS FOR PHARMACEUTICAL APPLICATIONS

Practical guidelines on the design and use of Isolators for the Aseptic Processing of Pharmaceuticals.

Edited for
The UK Pharmaceutical Isolator Group
by

Gerard Lee
B. Pharm, PhD, M.R. Pharm S, MRSC, C Chem.
North West Regional Health Authority, Liverpool.

Brian Midcalf
B. Pharm, M.R. Pharm S.
St. James's University Hospital, Leeds.

HMSO

First published 1994

ISBN 0 11 701829 5

FOREWORD

This is a revision of the document on the design and monitoring of isolators first published in 1993.[1] It has been extensively updated and several new sections have been added.

The working party that produced the first edition was originally convened following an initiative by NHS Regional quality control pharmacists in the UK, who after discussions with isolator manufacturers agreed to the formation of a special interest group to review the design and use of isolators for pharmaceutical applications. An open membership style was adopted for the group with representation from interested and relevant bodies. The first edition represented the outcome of the deliberations of quality control pharmacists, manufacturing pharmacists (hospital and industry), radiopharmacists, isolator manufacturers, the Medicines Control Agency and consultants or advisors in the field of isolation technology. Liaison with other bodies or specialist groups either nationally or internationally was encouraged and has developed over the last year.

A total of eleven meetings has taken place since the development of the group and, during the compilation of the second edition, a number of small project groups were created, who concentrated on specialist topics. Care was taken to ensure discussions to develop the paper were comprehensive and that a general agreement was reached which was acceptable to all members.

The general objective was to consider the standards necessary in the design, construction, commissioning and maintenance of isolators, and to prepare a comprehensive specification document for use by manufacturers and users. This document is a guide for intending purchasers and existing users. It is also a guide for manufacturers and those involved in standard setting and monitoring.

The principle objective of considering isolators for pharmaceutical use forms the subject of this publication but it is appreciated that other aspects of isolator design and use should eventually be considered. The different roles of isolators have been classified and potential users are encouraged to understand the principles used in this classification.

This guidance document has been sufficiently detailed to form the basis of a standards document that could be adopted by the BSI, CEN or ISO committees. Other countries have expressed support and interest and further liaison with such groups is to be encouraged.

It was originally intended that the first edition would be used for two years as an interim paper during which time comments were to be invited. Developments have been more rapid than anticipated and so the second edition has been produced ahead of schedule.

---

1. A specification for the design and monitoring of isolators. Quality Control Subcommittee of Regional Pharmaceutical Officers. 1993 Mersey Regional Health Authority.

Further comments on the content and format of the document will however be welcome. Users should send their comments to the Working Party Chairman who will continue to act as coordinator of such activities.

This second edition for pharmaceutical isolators has been expanded to include a number of appendices which cover more technical aspects of isolator design and performance monitoring. It has been very difficult to construct a paper that includes all existing isolators or all current manufacturers' designs. It is equally impossible for this paper to include all units that are in current use, most of which will have been constructed before these standards had been considered. Users of existing, older isolators should bear in mind the principles used in this paper and decide for which purpose their isolator is now suitable and whether some upgrading is appropriate. The critical areas of transfer into and out of the isolator have been considered and the many different ways of controlling this have been classified to include as many transfer devices as possible.

ACKNOWLEDGEMENT

The chairman wishes to acknowledge the collective skills and expertise shown by all members of the working party in compilation of this paper. The membership list is appended. Particular recognition is made to those involved with the practical organisation of the venues for the meetings, the financial support of such meetings, and the editorial effort of those involved in minutes and the actual paper, (which has had many revisions) without whose secretarial expertise this would not have been possible. Readers cannot be expected to appreciate the tremendous amount of discussion or the thought processes which have been undertaken in its production. The tolerance and forbearance of all those who contributed is recognised with gratitude. We wish to acknowledge also the assistance of the secretarial staff within the pharmacy department at Mersey Regional Health Authority and in particular the work of Tracy Nugent and Jean van Wijngaarden in typing and redrafting the document.

Brian Midcalf
Chairman, UK Pharmaceutical Isolator Group

MEMBERSHIP OF THE WORKING PARTY

Health Authority Members

Mr Brian Midcalf	Regional QA Pharmacist (Chairman)	St James University Hospital Beckett Street, Leeds LS9 7TF
Mr Ian Beaumont	Regional QA Pharmacist (Secretary)	North Western RHA
Mr Chris Adams	Production Pharmacist	Newcastle General Hospital
Dr Gerard Lee	Regional QA Pharmacist	Mersey RHA
Mr Tony Moore	Pharmacy Business Manager	Royal Hallamshire Hospital (Sheffield)
Mr Mitch Phillips	Regional QA Pharmacist	West Midlands RHA
Mr Charles Sampson	Principal Radiopharmacist	Addenbrookes Hospital, (Cambridge)
Dr Peter White	Managing Director	Nova Laboratories Ltd

MCA/Inspectorate

Mr Paul Hargreaves	Principal Medicines Inspector	MCA, London

Isolator Manufacturers

Mr Kevin Charlton	Mallinkrodt Medical
Mrs Caroline Coles	Institute of Containment and Isolation
Mr Tim Coles	MDH Consultant
Mr Trevor Drummond	Amercare Ltd
Mr Mike Foster	BassAire Ltd
Mr John Lees	MDH Contamination Control
Mr Graham Miles	Envair Ltd
Mr David Morley	Medical Air Technology Ltd
Mr Ian Munro	La Calhene (GB) Ltd
Mr John Neiger	Envair Ltd
Mr Bob Pringle	Halco Engineering Ltd
Dr David Watling	MDH Consultant

Pharmaceutical Industry

Mr Andrew Bill	Baxter Healthcare
Mr Russell Brammah	Consultant
Mrs Christine Burton	Fisons
Mrs Gillian Jordan	Smith Kline Beechams

CONTENTS

1 • INTRODUCTION

Isolator technology is now widely used and accepted for the aseptic processing of pharmaceuticals. The use of barrier systems offers improvements in the handling of pharmaceutical products in circumstances where product protection and the maintenance of asepsis, and/or operator protection and the control of hazardous substances are critical requirements. Isolators have several advantages over conventional clean rooms and laminar flow cabinets for aseptic preparation and dispensing of injections. They may be sited in an unclassified environment and still provide an acceptable level of sterility assurance for aseptic operations. Revenue costs can be reduced because a minimum amount of protective clothing is needed whereas the cost of clean room clothing can be high. Furthermore, their operator and product protection efficiency is not affected by air turbulence around the cabinet since the work area is totally enclosed, unlike vertical laminar flow drug safety cabinets, whose protection properties can be significantly reduced by air turbulence across the front opening of the cabinet. Isolators cannot however be regarded as totally sealed units since access to the controlled work space must be open when materials are transferred into and out of this area and the workspace is continuously supplied with HEPA filtered air. Other than this air supply, the controlled work space of the isolator will, when in use, be sealed from its background environment.

As a result of the economic and operational advantages of isolators, their use in hospital pharmacy in the UK is now widespread and over 400 are currently in use. They are designed and installed as individual units for aseptic preparation and dispensing of all forms of parenteral products and are commonly used in centralised cytotoxic reconstitution services, centralised IV additive services (CIVAS) and for the preparation of total parenteral nutrition (TPN) solutions.

Barrier systems and barrier technology also offer advantages to the pharmaceutical manufacturing industry for aseptic processing. Although the revenue and capital saving that hospitals have achieved may not be realised in industry, isolation technology can improve operator and product protection and increase sterility assurance of aseptic processing. Production lines with integrated isolation technology are now being introduced in the pharmaceutical industry. Isolators are also in use in microbiology departments for sterility testing, which is another area of work that relies heavily on an effective aseptic technique.

There is currently no National or International Standard for isolators for pharmaceutical use. Since one of their major advantages is that they can be custom built at reasonable cost for a defined purpose or service, a detailed specification would be impractical or restrictive. For any particular application, size, construction material, air flows, and pressure differentials can be optimised. Isolators are however expected to meet pre-defined performance criteria for aseptic operations and where applicable, operator protection. Consequently, it should be possible to define minimum operational parameters for their performance which will include air flow characteristics, and physical and microbiological standards of the internal and background environment.

The majority of isolators in the UK are used in hospital pharmacy departments. Therefore, this specification has been written from the hospital perspective. It is expected however that the design principles will be equally applicable to isolators and isolator systems that are intended for use in larger scale production facilities, although it is recognised that regulatory requirements for licensed manufacturing units will be the ultimate determinant factor in the design, use and monitoring of isolation technology in such units. These guidelines are intended therefore to be an information source for all staff involved in the design, commissioning, and use of isolators and isolator systems for pharmaceutical applications.

In planning a new isolator unit for pharmaceutical use, most of the factors to be considered in the siting, size, type of throughput, environmental controls, commissioning and monitoring can be identified from the document. Procedural aspects are left to the managers of the departments concerned in developing the service. It may be worth bearing in mind that careful consideration of the practical operation at an early stage in design and planning of new or revised service, should consider safety aspects on handling of raw materials and components. The disposal of waste generated from the packaging of components used in CIVAS or TPN units may not receive the attention it should at the design stage. One of the most difficult areas in the use of an isolator is the introduction of the raw materials and the passing out of finished components while maintaining the sterility of the critical working zone. The disposal of components and packaging generated in use and the method used for surface disinfection of such components should be considered at the planning stage of a new or revised service.

2 • DEFINITION OF TERMS

The following definitions apply to terms used within this document.

2.1 Isolator

A containment device which utilises barrier technology for the enclosure of a controlled work space.

2.2 Type 1 Isolator

An isolator primarily designed to protect the product from process-generated and external factors that would compromise its quality. However a degree of operator protection may also be achieved, if a physical barrier is maintained.

2.3 Type 2 Isolator

An isolator designed to protect the product from process-generated and external factors that would compromise its quality and to protect the operator from hazards associated with the product during operation and in the event of failure.

2.4 Air lock

An enclosed space with two or more doors and which is interposed between the controlled work space and the background environment of the isolator, for the purpose of controlling air flow between them and to facilitate the transfer of materials between them.

2.5 Alarm

An audible and/or visible signalling system which warns of a fault condition. It must incorporate a device to ensure that it cannot be cancelled until corrective action is taken.

2.6 Background Environment

The environment in which the isolator is sited. Background environments are categorised in table 3.

2.7 Breach Velocity

The air flow rate through an aperture sufficient to prevent movement of airborne particles in the opposite direction to the airflow. For the purposes of this definition, the aperture should be considered as a glove port or similar size opening.

2.8 Controlled Work Space

An enclosed space constructed and operated in such a manner and equipped with appropriate air handling and filtration systems to reduce to a pre-defined level the introduction, generation and retention of contaminants within it.

2.9 Critical Zone

That part of the controlled work space where containers are opened and product is exposed. Particulate and microbiological contamination should be reduced to levels appropriate to the intended use.

2.10 Decontamination

A process which reduces contaminating substances to a defined acceptance level.

2.10.1 *Sanitization*

That part of decontamination which reduces viable micro-organisms to a defined acceptance level.

2.10.2 *Particulate Decontamination*

That part of decontamination which reduces visible and sub-visible particle levels to a defined acceptance level.

2.10.3 *Chemical Decontamination*

That part of decontamination which reduces chemical contamination to a defined acceptance level.

2.11 Docking Device

A sealable chamber which can be completely removed from or locked onto an isolator and then opened without contamination passing into, or out of, the controlled work space or the chamber.

2.12 Exhaust Filter

A filter through which the exit stream of air from an isolator passes.

2.13 HEPA (High Efficiency Particulate Air) Filter

Filters with no greater than 0.003% penetration of 0.5µm particles when tested according to BS 3928.

2.14 Latched System

An alarm system that continues to indicate an alarm condition until reset by the operator.

2.15 Laminar Flow

Airflow in which the entire body of air within a confined area moves with uniform velocity along parallel flow lines.

Note: May also be referred to as *unidirectional flow*.

2.16 Radiation Protection System

A system which reduces to an acceptable level the exposure of the operator and the external environment to radiated emissions from radionuclides in accordance with the recommendations of the National Radiation Protection Board.

2.17 Safe Change Facility

A system which enables filters or filter systems to be changed without hazard to the operator and the background environment.

2.18 Sterilization

The process applied to a specified field which inactivates viable microorganisms and thereby transforms the non-sterile field into a sterile one.

2.19 Transfer Chamber

A device which facilitates the transfer of goods into or out of the controlled workspace whilst minimising the transfer of contaminants.

2.20 Transfer Hatch

See transfer chamber.

2.21 Transfer Isolator

A separate isolator which can be fixed or removable and which is attached to the main operational unit, acting as a complete transfer device.

2.22 Transfer Device

A device, which can be fixed or removable, which allows materials to be transferred into or out of the controlled work space.

2.23 Transfer Port

See transfer chamber.

2.24 Transfer System

The process of transfer of materials into and out of the isolator through a transfer device.

2.25 Turbulent Flow

A flow of air which is non-laminar.

3 • DESIGN PRINCIPLES

Although the specifications should not be restrictive, there are basic design parameters to which isolators should conform.

3.1 Air input may be laminar flow, turbulent flow, or a combination of the two.

3.2 The critical zone of the controlled workspace should be equivalent to the EC Grade A, but the airflow in the critical zone need not be laminar flow (see 3.3).

3.3 If the isolator is not supplied with a laminar air flow system, tests should be performed so as to confirm that only air complying with the requirements of EC Grade A is supplied to the critical zone. Air should be effectively swept from the controlled work space and standing vortices and stagnant areas should not exist.

3.4 Type 2 isolators should operate under negative pressure.

3.5 Type 2 isolators for use with radiopharmaceuticals should incorporate an appropriate radiation protective system against ionising radiations.

3.6 For operator protection, in the event of a breach in type 2 isolators a minimum breach velocity of 0.7m sec^{-1} should be maintained.

3.7 The transfer of materials into and out of the controlled work space is a critical factor of the isolator's operation. The transfer device separates the background environment from the Grade A controlled workspace. It should be designed such that it does not compromise the Grade A controlled environment. To this end an interlocked device will provide greater security. The size of the transfer device should be sufficient to allow all necessary materials and equipment to be passed through.

Note: Commissioning studies should include tests to confirm that contaminants will not pass from the transfer device into the controlled work area. A fully validated transfer procedure should be written.

3.8 All internal surfaces should be accessible to the operator for cleaning and disinfection purposes without compromising the isolator's integrity. They should be resistant to corrosion by cleansing and disinfecting agents and should be capable of withstanding gaseous disinfection or sterilisation.

3.9 The pressure differential between the Grade A controlled work space and the background environment should be continuously monitored and pressure sensors should be alarmed to indicate when the pressure difference is outside defined limits. The alarm should be visible and/or audible to the operator. For type 1 isolators the minimum alarm pressure differential should be set at 20 pascals.

Note: Rapid glove withdrawals will have a significant effect on isolator operating pressure. Operational procedures should take account of this and rapid withdrawals should be avoided. The alarm system should be capable of detecting these rapid pressure changes.

3.10 Air flow and the air change rate within the isolator should be monitored continuously. Input and/or output air flows should be monitored continuously and should be alarmed to indicate when the flow is outside defined limits. The alarm should be a latched system.

3.11 All filters in isolators in which hazardous substances are handled must have a safe change facility. Both the manufacturer and the user should be made aware of the risks associated with changing filters.

3.12 All exhaust (or re-circulated) air should pass through one or more HEPA filters. Extract air from type 2 isolators should normally be ducted to the outside through one or more HEPA filters and other necessary adsorption media (e.g. carbon). Where isolators are used infrequently or low levels of hazardous materials are handled, then the exhaust air may be re-circulated into the background environment through two HEPA filters in series provided the risk has been assessed and has been shown to be low risk. (For further details of exhaust filters see also appendix 5).

3.13 When designing isolators, consideration should be given to optical clarity, lighting, noise levels, humidity, electrical safety, temperature, vibration, ergonomics and the comfort of the operator(s).

3.14 Pressure differentials and the direction of air flow should be such that when the access between the transfer system and the controlled work space is open, contaminants will not pass into the controlled workspace and, additionally in type 2 isolators, operator protection is also maintained.

3.15 If a fixed transfer device has its own air supply it should be HEPA filtered.

3.16 The air change rate in all parts of the isolator system should be sufficient to maintain the defined grade of environment during use.

The air change rate will be such that any unfiltered air that enters the isolator or transfer device will be purged from the system within 5 minutes.

3.17 The laminar flow air velocity should be within the range 0.3–0.6m sec^{-1} at all times and no value may deviate from the mean by more than ± 20%.

3.18 The monitoring system should be capable of indicating a partial blockage of inlet and exhaust filters which would necessitate their replacement.

3.19 The fan should not be capable of damaging the filters in their maximum loaded state.

3.20 Isolators should have the facility to enable routine leak testing and particle counts to be carried out in the isolator itself and in its transfer devices. Where access points are provided for test equipment they should be labelled.

3.21 The isolator should be designed so that the HEPA filters can be integrity tested *in situ*.

4 • SITING OF ISOLATORS

4.1 Isolator(s) should be sited in a dedicated room(s) used only for the isolator and its ancillary equipment and related activities. The interior surfaces of the room (walls, floors, ceiling) should be smooth, free from cracks and open joints. They should not shed particulate matter and should allow easy and effective cleaning and sanitization.

4.2 The classification of the background environment in which the isolator is located will depend upon the design and operational characteristics of the isolator. When deciding on the siting of isolators, consideration should be given to the following:

The type of isolator—type 1/type 2

The transfer system—see appendix 1

The level and frequency of use i.e. dispensing/preparation/manufacture

In order to address these variables, isolators have been classified according to the transfer system. Details of the different transfer systems and the corresponding transfer devices are shown in appendix 1. The background environment for the isolator can then be categorised as I,II,III,IV, V or EC Grade A-D depending upon the transfer system and the use to which the isolator will be put (tables 1 and 2).

4.3 The definitions of air quality categories I–V are given in table 3. The categories have been defined according to their permitted levels of viable and non viable particles. For comparative purposes, the requirements of the different environmental classifications from commonly quoted standards documents are also included in the table.

It should be noted that the levels of viable micro-organisms for categories II–IV of the background environment are more stringent than the nearest grade of air quality specified in the EC. GMP.

4.4 For pharmaceutical applications the major criterion upon which the background environment is categorised should be the risk of microbiological contamination of the product. For this reason the environment has been classified in this document according to the number of viable organisms that can be detected.

It is recognised however that environmental testing is not a guarantee that environmental quality is maintained. Procedures and quality systems should be used to provide the necessary level of quality assurance.

4.5 It should be noted that EC GMP requirements for radiopharmaceuticals currently specify a Grade D external background environment for the manufacture of radiopharmaceuticals.

4.6 Aseptic preparation activities in hospitals in the UK are exempted from the licensing requirements of the Medicines Act provided specific criteria are met[2]. The definitions of the background environment for isolators used for preparation activities are conditional upon compliance with these criteria.

Preparation is understood to mean preparation for stock or preparation for dispensing in accordance with these MCA guidelines[2].

---

2. Guidance to the NHS on the licensing requirements of the Medicines Act. September 1992, Medicines Control Agency, London

5 • THE ENVIRONMENT

5.1 Physical Testing

The particle counts of the environment within the controlled work space, critical zone and the transfer device should be within EC Grade A in the non-operational state.

5.2 Microbiological Levels

The environment inside the critical zone of the controlled work space should be within EC Grade A during operations and that inside the transfer device for a type 1 isolator should be within EC Grade B when in use. The transfer device for a type 2 isolator should return to a grade B environment before the access to the controlled work space is opened.

Because of the imprecision of the methods, the expected low levels of contamination and the natural variability of the levels, the data require most careful analysis. It is recommended that target levels are established corresponding to those give in table 4. If formal statistical analysis is carried out, these levels represent 95% confidence limits. Alternatively trend analysis should be performed on the data. Exceeding target levels on isolated occasions may not require more action than examination of control systems. However, the frequency of exceeding the limit should be examined and should be low. If the frequency is high or shows an upward trend, then action should be taken.

Note 1: The limits applied to the transfer device will be determined by the validation data for the transfer system. The limit suggested is that for a grade B clean room.

Note 2: It is recognised that in-use monitoring of transfer devices is not always practical, particularly with type 2 isolators. Nonetheless, the integrity of the transfer system during the transfer process should be monitored regularly using a suitable method.

6 • FREQUENCY OF MONITORING

6.1 The recommended minimum frequency of monitoring for isolators and the room in which they are sited is given in table 5, 6 and 7. Depending upon the design, size and application of the isolator it may be necessary to alter the frequencies of testing. Validation following commissioning will require more frequent monitoring. Equally, if, over a period of time, it can be demonstrated that the controlled environment conditions are maintained, then the frequency may be reduced. Test methods for microbiological and physical monitoring are described in appendices 2, 3 and 4.

6.2 The number of settle plates and surface samples will depend upon the size and construction of the isolator and its background environment. The monitoring programme should be devised following commissioning studies.

6.3 There should be, for each installation, a written operating procedure that details the nature and frequency of all tests to be undertaken as part of an environmental monitoring programme.

6.4 When measuring the inlet air velocity for vertical laminar flow isolators, record the downward air velocity and, for turbulent flow isolators, record the number of air changes per hour.

6.5 In addition to in-use surface samples, microbiological surface samples should also be taken after sanitisation or cleaning, to validate the process.

7 • GLOVES AND GAUNTLETS

All isolators are accessed via a glove port using a suitable glove system. The glove system is a gauntlet or glove and sleeve arrangement which is designed to maintain the aseptic environment within the isolator. Several types of gauntlets and glove and sleeve arrangements, made from various materials, are available and careful selection will be necessary.

It is recommended that gloves and gauntlets used with isolators should, as a minimum, comply with the limits for perforations specified in BS 4005: 1984, the British Standard for sterile latex surgeons gloves.

Changing gloves and gauntlets presents a risk to the integrity of the isolator system. Operators should be aware of this risk and the change over process should be validated.

Operatives should undertake a hand disinfection procedure before using the isolator and, where practical, a sterile pair of latex examination gloves should be worn.

7.1 Gauntlets

These are one piece, full arm-length gloves. They are available in a range of materials. Manufacturers may not be aware of the need for stringent testing for perforations during manufacturing, unless the gauntlets have been produced specifically for use with isolators.

They are usually changed on a weekly or longer basis due to the high cost, resulting in a potential risk of drug penetration. In addition general hygiene may be poor as a number of operators will use the same glove. For these reasons, double-gloving is generally used. However, as gauntlets do not fit well, particularly under conditions of negative pressure, operator sensitivity will be reduced.

Gauntlets are usually thicker than surgeons' latex gloves, which may offset the risk of drug penetration to a degree. They are not normally available pre-sterilised.

7.2 Gloves and sleeves

These are multi-component systems consisting generally of a replaceable sleeve piece, a connecting cuff piece and the glove. The sleeve should be mechanically strong enough to remain in position without deterioration throughout its period of use. It should not be too rigid for comfortable working and should be resistant to chemical attack. The cuff piece should allow an easy, safe, aseptic, glove change-over.

The glove and sleeve arrangement allows gloves of an appropriate specification, particularly with respect to perforations and pinholes, to be used. It should allow the operator to change gloves as frequently as required. This enables gloves of the correct size to be used and the glove material can be altered as necessary. Consequently, the risk of drug penetration can be minimised and general hygiene can be improved. A fresh, sterile pair of gloves should be fitted for each operator working session. If the isolator is to be used for the radiolabelling of blood cells, a fresh sterile pair of gloves should be fitted for each blood sample. Double gloving using latex examination gloves may offer additional protection or simplify working practices.

TABLE I

SITING OF TYPE I ISOLATORS:
DEFINITION OF THE BACKGROUND ENVIRONMENT OF THE ISOLATOR ACCORDING TO THE TRANSFER SYSTEM AND THE APPLICATION OR USE OF THE ISOLATOR

ISOLATOR TRANSFER SYSTEM	ACTIVITY		
	DISPENSING	PREPARATION	MANUFACTURE
A	I	I	EC grade B
B	II	II	EC grade B
C1	III	III	III
D	IV	IV	IV
E/F	V	V	IV

TABLE 2

SITING OF TYPE 2 ISOLATORS: DEFINITION OF THE BACKGROUND ENVIRONMENT OF THE ISOLATOR ACCORDING TO THE TRANSFER SYSTEM AND THE APPLICATION OR USE OF THE ISOLATOR

ISOLATOR TRANSFER SYSTEM	ACTIVITY		
	DISPENSING	PREPARATION	MANUFACTURE
A	I	I	EC grade B
B	I	I	EC grade B
C1	I	I	EC grade B
C2/D	III	III	III*
E/F	IV	IV	III*

* Not applicable to radiopharmaceuticals, see 4.5

TABLE 3

DEFINITION OF AIR QUALITY CATEGORIES I–V. COMPARISON WITH EQUIVALENT INTERNATIONAL STANDARDS

CATEGORIES OF BACKGROUND ENVIRONMENT OF ISOLATOR	STANDARDS OF BACKGROUND ENVIRONMENT						NEAREST INTERNATIONAL STANDARDS			
	Particle Count (Particles M^{-3})				Viable Micro organisms		European GMP	Current British Standard BS5295:1989	Previous British Standard BS5295:1976	US Federal Standard 209E
	0.5 uM	5 uM	10 uM	25 uM	Airborne viable count colonies M^{-3})	Settle plate (colonies per plate)	*GRADE*	*CLASS*	*CLASS*	*CLASS*
	35	0						C		1
	350	0						D		10
I	3,500	0			5	1 per 2 plates	B	F	1	100
	35,000	200						H		1,000
	350,000	2,000	450				C	J	2	10,000
II	3,500,000	20,000	4,500	500	50	5	D	K	3	100,000
III	NS	200,000	45,000	5,000	100	10		L	4	
IV	NS	NS			500	50				
V		NS			NS	NS				

Note: 1 NS = Not Specified
2 See section 4 for further clarification of this table

TABLE 4

TARGET LEVELS OF VIABLE ORGANISMS IN ISOLATORS

	ISOLATOR	TRANSFER DEVICE
Active air sampler: min sample size 1 m^3	<1 per m^3	2 per m^3
Settle plate: 2h exposure	1 per 4 plates	1 per plate
Surface sample	zero	zero
Finger dabs	1 per plate	N/A

TABLE 5

RECOMMENDED MINIMUM FREQUENCIES OF MONITORING FOR DISPENSING OPERATIONS

Daily	Before dispensing starts, read and record all gauges. Confirm they are within limits and no alarm condition is indicated. Glove integrity test
Weekly	Finger dab plates Settle plates at marked sites in the isolator and transfer hatch. Alarm test User integrity test (type II isolators)
Monthly	User integrity test (all isolators) Airborne viable organisms at marked sites in the isolator Microbiological surface samples Settle plates at marked sites in the room in which the isolator is sited (where applicable)
Quarterly	Inlet air velocity into controlled work zone Airborne particle count in the isolator and the transfer device (where applicable) Airborne viable organisms at marked sites in the transfer hatch and isolator
6 monthly	Broth fill for all operators
Annual	HEPA filter integrity test Review staff training, all procedures and systems for continued applicability Breach velocity

TABLE 6

RECOMMENDED MINIMUM FREQUENCIES OF MONITORING FOR PREPARATION ACTIVITIES

Daily	Before preparation starts, record pressure drops across filters, isolator pressure differentials, and airflow rates. Confirm they are within limits and no alarm condition is indicated.
	Settle plates at marked sites in the isolator during each working session.
	Glove integrity test
Weekly	Finger dab plates
	Settle plates at marked sites in the isolator and transfer hatch
	Settle plates at marked sites in the room in which the isolator is sited (where applicable).
	Alarm test
	User integrity test (type II isolators)
Monthly	User integrity test (all isolators)
	Airborne viable organisms at marked sites in the transfer device (where applicable) and isolator
	Microbiological surface samples
	Airborne viable count at marked sites in the room in which the isolator is sited (where applicable)
Quarterly	Inlet air velocity into controlled work zone
	Airborne particle count in the isolator and the transfer device (where applicable)
	Broth fill for all operators
Annual	HEPA filter integrity test
	Review staff training, all procedures and systems for continued applicability.
	Breach velocity
	Leak detection test

TABLE 7

RECOMMENDED MINIMUM FREQUENCIES OF MONITORING FOR MANUFACTURING FACILITIES

Daily	Before production starts, record pressure drops across filters isolator pressure differentials and airflow rates. Confirm they are within limits and no alarm condition is indicated.
	Settle plates at marked sites in the isolator during each working session.
	Finger dabs after each working session.
	Glove integrity test.
Weekly	Settle plates at marked sites in the isolator and transfer hatch
	Settle plates at marked sites in the room in which the isolator is sited (where applicable)
	Alarm test
	User integrity test (type II isolators)
Monthly	User integrity test (all isolators)
	Airborne viable organisms at marked sites in the transfer chamber and isolator
	Microbiological surface samples
	Airborne viable count at marked sites in the room in which the isolator is sited (where applicable)
Quarterly	Inlet air velocity into controlled work zone
	Airborne particle count in the isolator and the transfer device (where applicable)
	Broth fill for all operators
Annual	HEPA filter integrity test
	Review staff training, all procedures and systems for continued applicability
	Breach velocity
	Leak detection test

APPENDIX I • ISOLATOR TRANSFER DEVICES

SCOPE

This appendix describes the different transfer devices that have been used in the past or could be developed for future use.

1 INTRODUCTION

Transfer devices can and have been designed in a variety of configurations. They can however be classified into different classes according to the risk to the integrity of the isolator during the transfer process. The devices that are currently available can be classified into one of seven categories.

2 THEORETICAL CONSIDERATION

The classification of the transfer device will determine the background environment of the isolator that will provide acceptable levels of product and operator protection. This classification will depend upon the ability to sanitize/sterilise the contents of the transfer device before allowing access to the controlled workspace.

Note: A diagram of each class of device is included with description. These diagrams are only intended to be illustrative examples of possible configurations.

3 THE DEVICES

Class Description | **Direction of Inward Transfer ▶**

Background Environment ▼ | *Controlled Work Space* ▼

A Transfer devices through which, when operated in accordance with the validated transfer procedure, air can flow freely between the background environment and the controlled work space.
Examples: Doors, Zips, Velcro, Poppers and "Jam Pot" Covers.

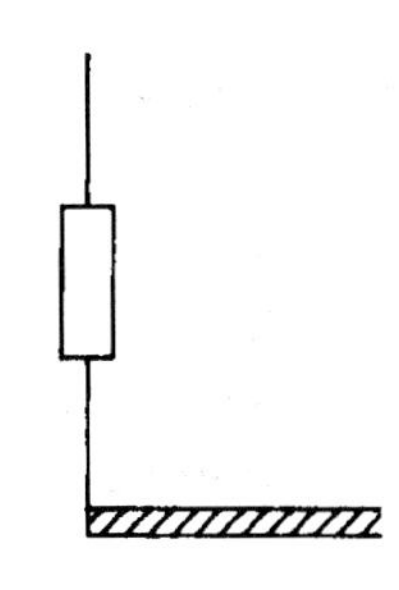

B Transfer devices which, when operated in accordance with the validated transfer procedure, do not permit the direct passage of air between the background environment and the controlled work space, but which are so constructed that air from the background environment can be trapped and then released into the controlled work space and air from the controlled work space can be trapped and released into the background environment.
Examples: Double Door Sealed Transfer Chambers, Bagging Ports, Telescopic Waste Ports and Simple Docking Devices.

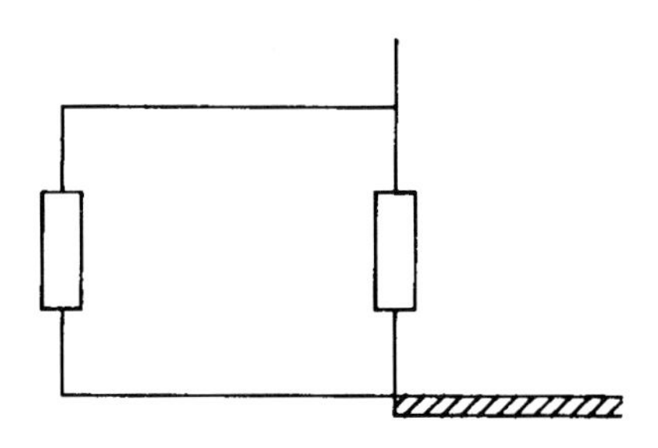

KEYS TO DIAGRAMS

Double Door Port

Sealed Door

HEPA Filters

Valve

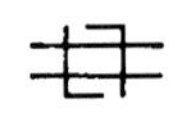

Gassing Point (quick disconnect coupling)

Work surface of controlled workspace

Class	Description	Direction of Inward Transfer ▶
		Background Environment ▼ *Controlled Work Space* ▼

C1 Transfer devices with doors and HEPA filters which when used in a type 1 isolator and operated in accordance with the validated transfer procedure do not allow unfiltered air from the background environment to reach the controlled work space but which might allow unfiltered air from the controlled work space to reach the background environment. Such transfer devices are not suitable for type 2 Isolators because they would allow unfiltered air from the background environment to reach the controlled work space. They are not recommended where operator protection is required in type 1 Isolators.
Examples: Single Filtered Transfer Chambers.

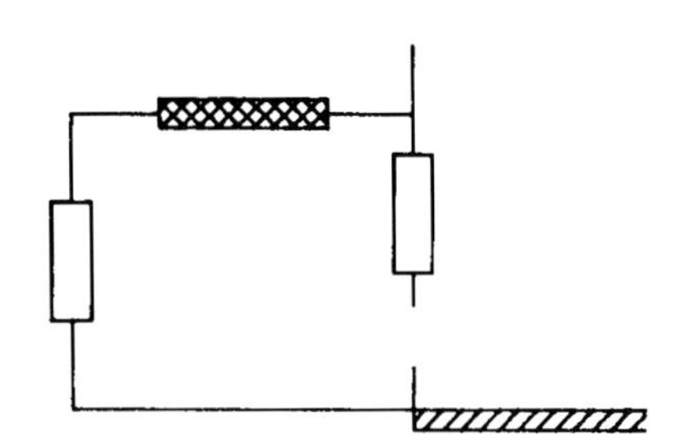

KEYS TO DIAGRAMS

Double Door Port

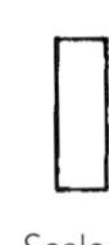

Sealed Door

HEPA Filters

Valve

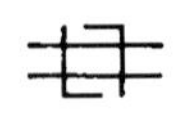

Gassing Point (quick disconnect coupling)

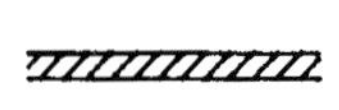

Work surface of controlled workspace

Class	Description	Direction of Inward Transfer ▶
		Background Environment ▼ *Controlled Work Space* ▼
C2	Transfer devices with doors and HEPA filters which when used in a type 2 Isolator and operated in accordance with the validated transfer procedure do not allow unfiltered air from the background environment to reach the controlled work space (such air passing straight into the space below the work surface of the controlled work space and then through a HEPA filter) or unfiltered air from the controlled work space to reach the background environment. Such transfer devices are not appropriate for use with a type 1 isolator. *Examples: Single Filtered Transfer Chambers.*	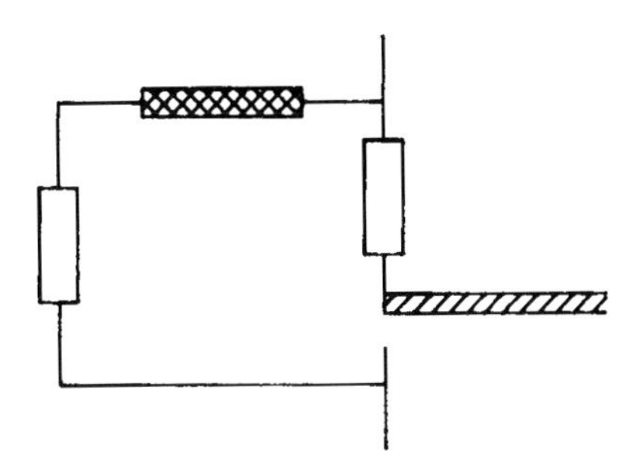

KEYS TO DIAGRAMS

Double Door Port

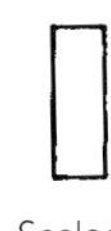

Sealed Door

HEPA Filters

Valve

Gassing Point (quick disconnect coupling)

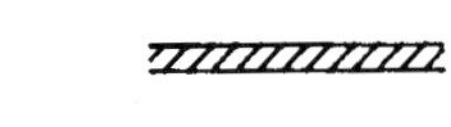

Work surface of controlled workspace

Class	Description	Direction of Inward Transfer ▶
		Background Environment ▼ *Controlled Work Space* ▼
D	Transfer devices with doors and HEPA filters which when operated in accordance with the validated transfer procedure do not permit unfiltered air from the background environment to reach the controlled work space , or unfiltered air from the controlled work space to reach the background environment. *Examples: Double Filter Transfer Chambers, Certain Transfer Isolators.*	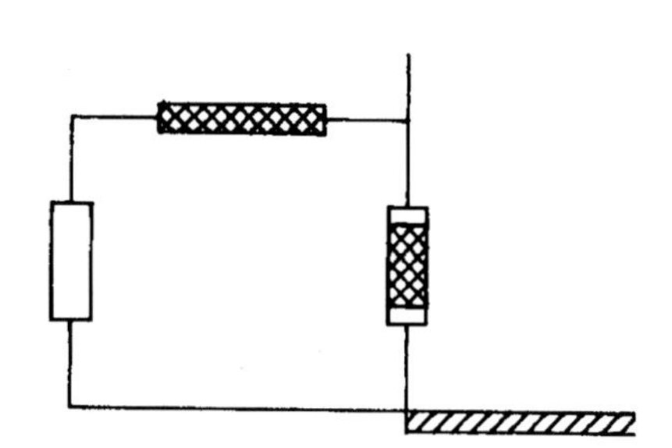

KEYS TO DIAGRAMS

Double Door Port

Sealed Door

HEPA Filters

Valve

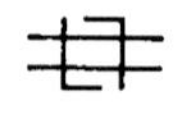

Gassing Point (quick disconnect coupling)

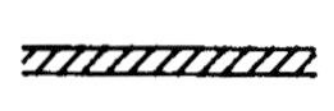

Work surface of controlled workspace

Class	Description	Direction of Inward Transfer ▶
		Background Environment ▼ *Controlled Work Space* ▼
E	Transfer devices which are subject to sanitization together with their contents, if any, before being opened into other areas which have been subject to sanitization. *Examples: Gassable/Autoclavable Transfer Devices including certain Transfer Isolators and Docking Devices, Permanently Connected Autoclaves, Permanently Connected Heat Tunnels.*	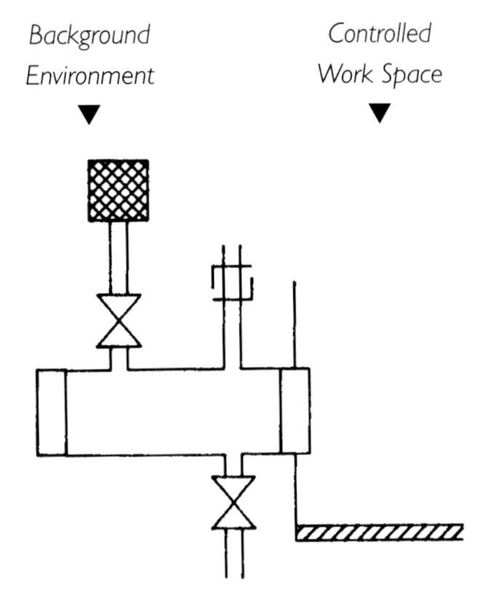

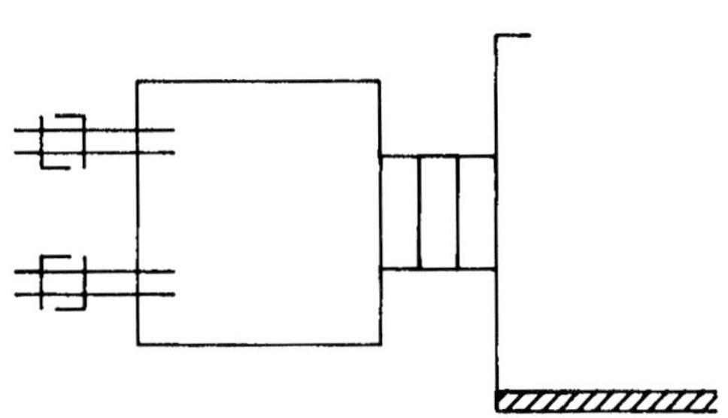

F Any transfer device (including all of the above) which opens into an Isolator which is subsequently sealed, is subjected to sanitization before processing commences and is kept sealed until processing is completed. In the case of type 2 Isolators, the Isolator remains sealed until subjected to whatever decontamination is appropriate on completion of processing.

KEYS TO DIAGRAMS

Double Door Port

Sealed Door

HEPA Filters

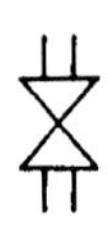

Valve

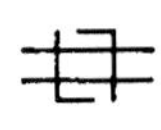

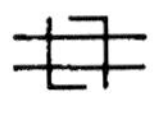

Gassing Point (quick disconnect coupling)

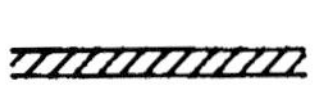

Work surface of controlled workspace

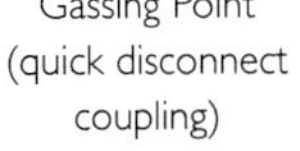

APPENDIX 2 • MICROBIOLOGICAL TEST PROCEDURES

SCOPE

This appendix suggests test procedures for the microbiological monitoring programme described in tables 5, 6 and 7.

1 INTRODUCTION

The microbiological monitoring requirements will vary depending upon the size of the facilities and the scale and type of operation. The test methods should be designed to complement these requirements. The following practical considerations should act as guidance when designing test protocols and procedures.

2 TEST METHODS

2.1 General

The person responsible for microbiological surveillance should acquaint himself with the naturally occurring micro-organisms that are or may become present in the isolator system and surrounding environment. The choice of suitable microbiological media and culture conditions should reflect the indigenous microbiological population. The following suggestions utilise tryptone soya medium because this is suitable for a wide range of microorganisms. However, if, for example, waterborne organisms are likely to be present, a yeast extract medium may be more suitable.

A plan of the isolator should be prepared with coded positions for settle plate, swabbing and air sampling sites. Production units should have alarm timers or similar devices so that the period of plate exposure remains constant.

For all tests the following evaluations should be carried out:

- Examine the cultures during incubation and upon completion. The microbiologist should take appropriate action when changes in the normal population are detected, and microorganisms that represent a particular threat to the operation (e.g. bacterial spore formers etc.) are found to be present.
- The date and time of the test, coded position of each sample, the number of colonies found, or presence of turbidity in broth, should be recorded, together with any relevant comments concerning the types of microorganisms present.
- When alert limits are exceeded, a more detailed characterisation of the microorganisms is appropriate (e.g. to genus or relevant group) together with a proper record of the ensuing investigation, findings, and agreed corrective action.

2.2 Settle Plates

Expose coded and dated, sterile, tryptone soya agar plates for two hours at all test sites within the isolator. Incubate at the appropriate temperature for up to five days, or as otherwise chosen by the microbiologist.

2.3 Surface Samples

Take surface samples at coded sites using sterile contact plates or sterile moistened swabs. Where swabs are used, recovery may be accomplished by streaking onto tryptone soya agar, or suspension (dissolving in the case of soluble swabs) in a suitable sterile diluent and subsequent viable counting of the resultant liquid. Incubate at the appropriate temperature for up to five days or as otherwise selected by the microbiologist.

Note: Each sample site should be sanitised to remove any material transferred to it during the sampling process.

2.4 Active Air Sampling

The choice of equipment for carrying out active air sampling is at the discretion of the microbiologist. The wide variety of impact and agar impingement samplers all have their advocates and perceived advantages and disadvantages.

The various air samplers in common use have different sampling efficiencies and so the limits will differ for individual devices. The manufacturer's instructions should be followed or, if the sampler is operated for longer than its recommended time, the procedure should be validated.

Samples should be taken at the coded sites.

Where the test utilises standard plates or strips, these should be incubated at the appropriate temperature for up to five days, or as otherwise selected by the microbiologist.

2.5 Finger Dabs

The point during the production process that finger dabs should be carried out should be defined e.g. at a break time or end of a day's work.

Gently press the tips of each finger and thumb onto the surface of a tryptone soya agar plate. Incubate at the appropriate temperature for up to five days.

2.6 Broth, or Media Fills (Media Process Simulation)

The broth fill is a validation procedure that challenges both operator and facilities. The purpose of broth fills is to simulate routine aseptic operations in such a way as to produce broth filled units that can be tested for microbiological contamination.

For each process, the risk of microbiological contamination will differ depending upon the facilities and the procedures that are used. The microbiologist should analyse the operations and devise a broth fill sequence that reflects normal or worst case practices. It should be directly relatable to the process and the number of units filled should represent a normal batch size.

The type of broth used is often sterile tryptone soya broth that may be presented in double strength to allow for dilution with buffer, saline, or water to simulate the process. Any suitable liquid culture medium may however be used but the ability of the broth to support growth should be demonstrated.

Incubate at the designated temperature for up to 14 days or as otherwise chosen by the person responsible for microbiology.

If the final container is part filled ensure all surfaces are in contact with broth at some stage during incubation.

A procedure should define actions following positive results and should focus initially on whether the facility/equipment or operator practices are failing.

APPENDIX 3 • PHYSICAL TEST PROCEDURES

SCOPE

The appendix will describe test procedures that can be used to perform the physical tests in tables 5, 6 and 7.

1 INTRODUCTION

Since the test procedures will depend upon the design and configuration of the isolator, it is not possible to specify one method that would be suitable for all isolators. These methods therefore will give details of the aspects of the test protocol that are common to all isolators.

Note: All instrumentation on isolators should be calibrated in accordance with the isolator manufacturer's instructions at least annually.

All test equipment for testing isolators should be calibrated in accordance with the test equipment manufacturer's instructions at least annually.

2 ALARM TEST

All alarms should be tested according to manufacturers' test protocols.

3 LEAK TESTS

(*see appendix 4*)

4 INLET AIR VELOCITY

For turbulent isolators the volume flow rate should be indicated by manufacturer's instrumentation. A protocol should be available to allow instrumentation to be cross checked against a volumetric measurement.

For laminar flow isolators the downflow velocity should be measured every three months using an anemometer in accordance with BS.5726 Pt. 1. Appendix H but with the sample positions in a horizontal plane 100 mm below the HEPA filter face.

5 AIRBORNE PARTICLE COUNTS

Airborne particle counts in the isolator and its transfer devices should be measured and recorded every three months using a particle counter in accordance with BS.5295 Pt. 1

Appendix E and using sampling points that are appropriate to the design of the isolator. In addition airborne particle counts should also be measured and recorded in the background environment, when these are category I, II, or III.

6 HEPA FILTER INTEGRITY TESTS

HEPA filter integrity tests by means of an aerosol generator and detector should be carried out annually in accordance with BS.5295 Pt. I Appendix C.

For filters that cannot be scanned eg. cartridge filters, the aerosol challenge should be applied upstream of the filter by means of an aerosol generator, and particle counts measured downstream of the filter at fixed test points using a suitable test apparatus.

7 BREACH VELOCITY

With the cabinet running, measure the air velocity at the centre of an open glove port.

APPENDIX 4 • INTEGRITY TESTS

SCOPE

This appendix suggests test procedures for the detection of leaks which may compromise integrity in totally enclosed isolator systems. Different tests protocols are given for the glove system and for the isolator in general.

1 GLOVES, GAUNTLETS AND GLOVE/SLEEVE ASSEMBLIES ON ISOLATORS AND ON HALF-SUITS FITTED TO ISOLATORS

1.1 Introduction

Damage to, or misfitment of the glove system may compromise the internal air quality of the isolator.

Any ingress of contamination through a glove system will adversely affect the critical zone in both Type 1 and Type 2 isolators. The risk however is greater in isolators operating at negative pressure.

As the gloves/gauntlets could provide a potentially high risk of contamination, the integrity of the glove system should be tested on a sessional basis and when new gloves or gauntlets are fitted.

Note: During extended sessions or if an incident occurs, it may be necessary to repeat the test during the session.

Glove systems can be tested for leakage by simple methods. The sensitivity of the test is affected by the operating or test pressure of the isolator, but the principle can be applied to all systems.

1.2 Test Procedures

1.2.1 *General*

Test protocols should include careful visual inspection at the beginning and end of each work session. Where a work session is over an extended period, then additional visual inspection will be required at regular intervals during the session.

A standard operational procedure must be available, which clearly defines the actions required in the event of a known or suspected breakdown of a glove system during operational usage.

1.2.2 *Test Principle*

If the glove system can be sealed off, the pressure change within the sealed zone can be monitored and the extent of leakage identified by the rate of change of pressure towards equilibrium.

The following protocols can be used as tests for leaks in glove systems.

Protocol 1—Glove leak test: type 1 and type 2 isolators
Using a plate, seal off the glove system across the glove port or shoulder ring of the isolator. Measure the air pressure trapped within the glove system using a manometer and monitor the pressure change caused by the equilibrium process. The rate of change of pressure registered on the manometer can provide direct assessment of the leakage rate in a known system. The more sensitive the manometer, the more sensitive the test. With type 1 isolators it will be necessary to inflate the glove to a pressure higher than the isolator pressure until it adopts the shape it would have in use, before the test is carried out.

This test can provide an indication of a leak within one minute. It may be usable therefore as a sessional test performed by isolator operators.

A leak in the gauntlet or glove system of a type 2 isolator can expose the critical workspace to potentially contaminated air from the background environment. If this test reveals that there is a leak, then a further visual test can be carried out using a smoke pencil to identify the strength and direction of the leakage jet. (See also 2.2.2. of this appendix).

Protocol 2—Glove leak test: type 2 isolators only
Place a flexible diaphragm across the glove port or shoulder ring trapping air within the glove system at the background air pressure.

If there is leakage, then the trapped air will gradually equilibrate with the internal negative pressure of the isolator and the diaphragm will adopt a visible concave shape.

Visualising or mechanically measuring the change in shape of the diaphragm will allow quite small levels of leakage to be identified. It may be difficult to establish the sensitivity of this test for individual units, therefore an overnight test may be required to identify smaller leaks and simple pass/fail criteria applied.

2 ISOLATORS

2.1 Introduction

The significance of leakage into and out of isolators varies with the type of isolator, its location and its application.

When specifying isolators, the acceptable leakage rate should be established between the isolator manufacturer and the user. Tests should then be specified to ensure that the isolator maintains the agreed design characteristics. The pass/fail criteria should be based upon the volume leakage rate per hour, expressed as a fraction of the isolator volume, at the maximum operating pressure differential of the isolator. The criteria should take into account a sufficient safety margin to ensure that clear failure of a test will be reached well before the isolator integrity falls outside the defined limits.

Air leaks can occur in a number of ways. Room air can bypass HEPA filters if the seals are damaged or defective, e.g. due to degradation of the sealant caused by disinfectant agents, or loosening of the filter clamping mechanism by vibration. Induction leaks in a type 1 isolator and in-leakage in a type 2 isolator are capable of compromising the sterility of the controlled work space of the isolator presenting a risk of contamination to the processes and materials therein. Out-leakage in a type 1 isolator is capable of contaminating the isolator background environment and any personnel therein. This is only of concern if substances hazardous to health such as cytotoxic preparations or gaseous disinfectants are present in the isolator.

2.2 Theoretical Considerations

2.2.1 *Induction Leaks in Type 1 Isolators*

An induction leak occurs when the velocity of air across an orifice creates a depression which will induce an airflow through the orifice. This is also known as the "venturi effect".

The internal air quality of systems operating at nil differential pressures or under very low positive pressures could be compromised by induction leakage. It can be demonstrated that such leakage will not occur unless the dynamic pressure of the moving air inside the isolator (given by the formula below) is greater than the static pressure of the isolator above the background environment.

$$\text{Dynamic pressure} = \frac{d \times u^2}{2}$$

where d = density in kg m^{-3}
u = velocity in m sec^{-1}

By this formula, for example, the risk of an induction leak occurs when the isolator pressure is less than 20Pa above that of the background environment and the air velocity at any of the surfaces surrounding the controlled work space is greater than 6 m/sec.

It should be noted that the positive pressure in a Type 1 isolator can be dramatically and momentarily reduced by the rapid withdrawal of any item, eg a glove/sleeve system or gauntlet. This sudden reduction of pressure will be much more significant in a small isolator than a large isolator and should be taken into account in assessing the potential effect of induction leaks.

Providing that the operating pressure of the Type 1 isolator remains high enough to overcome the aggregate of these two effects (namely induction leaks and glove withdrawals), there will then be no direct airborne in-leakage in a Type 1 isolator.

2.2.2 *In-leakage in Type 2 Isolators*

The main risk of failure in Type 2 isolators is product contamination.

The internal air quality change resulting from an in-leakage into an isolator depends on many factors including the design and size of the isolator, the type of airflow, the air-change rate, and the size, position, direction and nature of the leak. There is a general equation for estimating the likely internal air quality change resulting from an in-leakage. As this equation assumes instant perfect mixing and disregards most of the other factors mentioned, it must only be used in conjunction with an assessment of the effect of these factors on the result in each practical situation.

The equation is as follows:

$$Q_R = \frac{Q_L \times V_i}{F}$$

where Q_R is the internal air quality change measured in particles/m^3

Q_L is the background air quality measured in particles/m^3

V_i is the volume in-leakage/hour expressed as a fraction of the isolator volume at the maximum operational pressure differential.

F is the dilution factor expressed as the number of volume air changes/hour

This equation, is only approached in practice when the airflow in the controlled work-space is very turbulent and the velocity of in-leakage is very small. This occurs if there is a significant resistance in the leakage path, e.g. a poorly sealed joint or gasket.

The following is an example for a typical installation:

Theoretical analysis using this formula shows that for a turbulent flow Type 2 isolator operating at -30 pascals given an air delivery quality of 35 particles of 0.5um/m^3 (BS.5295 1989 Class C or US Fed.Std. 209 E Class 1) a background air quality of 35 million particles of 0.5um/m^3 which could be BS.5295 1989 Class L or, if such a class existed, US Fed.Std 209 E Class 1,000,000 and assuming perfect mixing (turbulence in the isolator), a leak of effective area 0.1mm^2 would not take a 1m^3 isolator outside correct operating criteria (BS.5295 1989 Class F or US Fed.Std. 209 E Class 100) if running at 25 air changes per hour or more.

Where the air velocity of a leak is large, an entirely different situation arises. A leak, which results from a hole in one of the thin walled components of the isolator such as a gauntlet or glove/sleeve system, or the envelope itself, may have an air velocity that is very large in relation to other airflows in the isolator whether these be turbulent or laminar. In this case a jet is formed which carries a long way into the isolator as it disperses.

The velocity of air through a hole in a thin wall is governed by the formula:

$$u = \sqrt{\frac{2\Delta p}{d}}$$

where u = Velocity in m $sec.^{-1}$
d = density in kg m^{-3}
Δp = static pressure differential across the hole in Pa.
(This formula is a re-arrangement of the formula in 2.2.1).

The volume flow rate of a leak is governed by the simple formula $v = u.a$

where v = volume flow rate in m^3 sec^{-1}
u = velocity in m sec^{-1}
a = effective area of leak in m^2 (known by engineers as the area of the Vena-contracta).

The following is an example of a typical situation:

> Theoretical analysis using these formulae shows that in a Type 2 isolator operating at -200 Pascals the air velocity of a leak through a hole is 18m sec^{-1}. (This compares for example with a typical laminar flow air velocity of 0.35m sec^{-1}.). If the leak has an effective area of 0.1mm^2, the volume flow rate of the leak is 0.0065m^3 hr^{-1}. If the air quality of the background environment is EC Grade D, i.e. each m^3 contains no more than 3,500,000 particles of 0.5um or above, 20,000 particles of 5um or above, or 500 viable micro organisms, then every hour no more than 22,750 particles of 0.5um or above, 130 particles of 5.0um or above and 3.25 viable micro organisms will enter the isolator. If the air-change rate of the isolator is 60 per hour, the number of particles present in 1m^3 of the isolator at any one time as a result of the leak will be 380 particles of 0.5um, 2 particles of 5um and 0.05 viable micro organisms. These particles and micro organisms will, however, be concentrated in a jet and the number of particles and micro organisms in the jet itself will be at a similar level to the background environment.

In this example therefore, the action to be taken as a result of detecting a leak of this type will depend on whether or not the jet has been in the direction of work or materials in the critical zone of the isolator.

It should be noted that the gauntlet or glove/sleeve system of an isolator is the part of the isolator that is most likely to develop a high velocity jet leak as described above, and tests similar to those described in section 1 of this appendix should be used to detect such leaks. The above example assumes that the quality of the air passing through the leak is that of the background environment. In practice, the air quality passing through a leak in a glove system will also be affected by the hand disinfection and gowning of the operator.

2.2.3 *Out-leakage in Type I isolators*

The main risk of failure in Type I isolators is the release of hazardous vapours and aerosols to the surrounding atmosphere. The same formulae as in 2.2.2 apply but with the airflow in the opposite direction.

The following is an example of a typical situation:

> Theoretical analysis using these formulae shows that with a Type I isolator operating at 30 Pascals the outward air velocity through a leak is $7 m.sec^{-1}$. If the leak has an effective area of $0.1 mm^2$ the volume flow rate of the leak of potentially contaminated air into the background environment is $0.00252 m^3 hr^{-1}$. If the inside of the isolator contains a gaseous contaminant (for example Hydrogen Peroxide when used as a gaseous disinfectant) at a concentration of 1000 ppm and the background environment in which the isolator is situated is a room with a volume of $360 m^3$ and an air-change rate of 20 per hour (typical for EC Grade D Air Classification) with 90% recirculation, the eventual dilution of the contaminant in the background environment, will be to a level of 0.0035 ppm.

2.3 Test Procedures

The following test procedures can be used as integrity leak tests for isolators. It is recognised also that alternative tests could be developed which may be equally or more appropriate.

Whatever test procedures are used, pass/fail criteria should be established and documented.

2.3.1 *Leak Detection Procedures*

The following is a non-exclusive list of test procedures that are suitable for the location of leaks at commissioning and at regular intervals thereafter.

Helium Test

Place a helium gas cylinder inside isolator (or connect to isolator), and close all the valves on the isolator. Seal all filter inlets and outlets. Bring the isolator up to a pressure 50% above normal operating pressure by releasing the helium. Scan all seals, joints, sleeves and half suit, if fitted, with a gas thermal conductivity tester. Any leaks will be indicated by a change in conductivity registered by the instrument.

When using helium, some method for circulating the air inside the envelope must be employed, e.g. a small fan unit.

Should a leak be detected the method of sealing would be dependant on the actual position and nature of the leak.

Dispersed oil particulate (DOP) aerosol test

This should be carried out in accordance with BS.5726 (1992) Pt.1 Appendix B.

Soap

This should be carried out in accordance with BS.5726 (1992) Pt.1 Appendix G.

2.3.2 *Pressure Tests*

A pressure test may be used at regular intervals to confirm the integrity of the envelope of the isolator. However great care must be taken in interpreting the results of a pressure test as changes in atmospheric pressure and especially temperature can have a very significant effect. The relationship between pressure, volume and temperature are governed by Boyle's law which is

$$\frac{PV}{T} = \text{constant}$$

where P = absolute pressure (in pascals)
V = volume (in m^3)
T = absolute temperature

Note: absolute pressure of the atmosphere is approximately 100,000 pascals.

The following are examples of the effects of this relationship.

- A 1°C rise in the internal temperature of a sealed isolator of fixed volume will cause a pressure increase of 350 pascals inside the isolator;
- A 1mm Hg (=1.36 millibar or 136 pascals) drop in the barometric pressure of the background environment of a sealed isolator of fixed volume causes a change of 136 pascals in the pressure differential between the isolator and its background environment.

The effects of temperature and pressure may appear singularly, act together or act against each other during the duration of a test and may mask the extent of any leak.

Protocol 1—Pressure decay test

Establish the designated test pressure and seal the inlets and outlets of the isolator. The pressure differential should be at least 50% above its normal operating value. The pressure decay should be recorded at regular intervals over the designated time.

The relationship between initial pressure differential, size of hole and rate of decay can be calculated using the formula 2.2.2.

Within the inaccuracies of this test the following assumptions and approximations can be made.

- The rate of change of absolute pressure of the isolator, expressed as a percentage change per unit time, is equal to the rate of volume change expressed as a percentage change per unit time.
- Temperature and air density remain constant (this is a very significant assumption).
- Pressure decay is linear for small changes in differential pressure.

A reference level of pressure decay should be established following a successful leak detection test and this value used as a standard comparitor in future tests.

For the reasons given in 2.3.2 the pressure decay test can only be relied upon to give an indication of a gross leak.

The following is an example of a typical situation:

> Theoretical analysis using the formulae and assumptions referred to shows that if the internal pressure of a Type 2 isolator is set to -275 pascals at the start of a pressure decay test and decays to -125 pascals after 30 minutes, the rate of pressure change and hence the rate of volume change is at the rate of 0.30% per hour. If the isolator volume is $3m^3$ the average flow rate through the leak is $0.009m^3/hr$. At a pressure differential of -200 pascals the air velocity through the leak is $18m.sec^{-1}$ and the effective area of the leak is therefore $0.14mm^2$.

Protocol 2—Pressure holding test

Establish the designated test pressure and seal the inlets and outlets of the isolator. Maintain the designated test pressure by means of a fan, blower or air-compressor connected to the isolator via a HEPA filter Measure the volume flow rate required to maintain the test pressure.

For the reasons given in 2.3.2 the pressure holding test can only be relied upon to give an indication of a gross leak.

2.3.3 *AECP (R) (Atomic Energy Code of Practice) 5 Type Test*[3]

Where an accurate test to confirm a very low acceptance level of % volume leakage is required (i.e. less than 0.05% per hour), then the Atomic Energy Code of Practice 5 Type Test[3] can be carried out by the manufacturer or test engineers. This takes into account the effects of atmospheric pressure change and temperature change as discussed above. The test also requires that these background test parameters are accurately monitored during the period of the test and any variations included in the calculations.

---

3. Leak tests for low working pressure containers. AEA Technology Code of Practice AECP (R) 5. 1990. AEA Technology Standards Office. Harwell, Oxfordshire.

3 FREQUENCY OF TESTING

The recommended minimum frequencies for all types of integrity testing are given in Tables 5, 6 and 7. The actual frequency for each installation should take into account the following:

- Application
- Risk to product
- Hazard to operator and background environment
- Quality of background environment
- Isolator design

APPENDIX 5 • EXHAUST FILTRATION

SCOPE

This appendix will describe the types of exhaust filters that can be used with isolators and will discuss criteria for their selection and use.

1 INTRODUCTION

Filtration devices can be generally categorised as:

- Pre Filters
- HEPA Filters
- Adsorption Filters
- Catalytic Filters

1.1 Pre Filters

Are usually of low efficiency and are intended to remove a significant proportion of larger particles from the airstream. The main function is to protect other filters and prolong their life.

1.2 HEPA Filter

These high efficiency filters will normally be constructed so as to be able to comply with BS 3928 which is a standard for filter efficiency tests. The expected performance standard is described earlier in section 2.13. Their primary intended use is to provide microbiological protection to the isolator on both inlet and outlet airflows. They may also be used in the exhaust outlet to reduce risk from hazardous particulate material in the exhaust airflow. The degree of protection offered will depend on the nature and particle size distribution of the contaminant. This is because unlike microbes, chemical contaminants can be gaseous, liquid or solid and of variable particle size.

1.3 Adsorption Filters

Often known as carbon filters or chemisorbant packs, these adsorption filters are intended to remove contaminants in the gaseous or vapour phase. They are not true filters and cannot be validated with respect to efficiency and effectiveness throughout their life. This is due to filter saturation and the channelling of the adsorption medium which can occur in use. Sufficient contact time must be allowed for adsorption to take place. Adsorption filters designed to remove specific chemicals can be obtained.

Verification of effectiveness is generally assessed by sampling the downstream airflow for the absence or presence of specific chemicals often using commercially available gas detection tubes.

1.4 Catalytic Filters

Consist of catalyst media which are designed to break down chemicals. These also are not true filters since they do not remove chemicals from the air stream but convert them to non-toxic products. An example would be a catalyst to degrade hydrogen peroxide. Verification of effectiveness will need to be demonstrated and regeneration may be required.

2 SELECTION AND USE OF FILTERS IN EXHAUST SYSTEMS

Pre filters would not normally be considered to provide a satisfactory level of protection to be used alone as an exhaust filter.

The type and number of exhaust filters will be dependant upon the potential risk of the activity being performed in the isolator, taking into account the hazard potential of any chemicals and the scale and frequency of the activity.

An example of a low hazard activity would be preparation of parenteral nutrition solutions. In this case, any exhaust filtration will primarily be to protect the isolator against ingress of microbes in the event of a system shut down.

An example of a high hazard potential activity would be a cytotoxic dispensing facility in daily use, providing a large number of doses. In this case a minimum requirement would be considered to be in line HEPA filtration with the extract ducted to atmosphere, or dual HEPA filters in series when air is recirculated into the room (see section 3.9). Consideration should also be given to the use of other filter types.

Where the hazard and risk is known, the filtration method should be chosen to deal specifically with that particular agent. It is prudent to seek the endorsement of a qualified Health and Safety advisor in the case of any doubt.

APPENDIX 6 • THE USE OF LIQUID CHEMICALS TO REDUCE THE LEVEL OF CONTAMINATION WITH MICRO-ORGANISMS INSIDE ISOLATOR SYSTEMS.

SCOPE

This section addresses disinfection procedures using chemical agents during which fluids are applied to surfaces with the intention of reducing the count of micro-organisms inside the controlled work space of an isolator to an appropriate and acceptable level.

1 INTRODUCTION

Most isolator systems will require two different procedures.

- A procedure for treatment of the impervious internal surfaces of the isolator and external surfaces of the resident equipment.
- A second procedure for treating surfaces of transient components which will be present in the isolator for a particular procedure.

The cleaning down of equipment and related treatments can employ a wide range of agents. Components and other aids to production are usually treated with alcohol-based preparations, which enable rapid evaporation of the solvent of such disinfectant agents and therefore facilitate a smooth, responsive work flow during production.

2 GENERAL

Unless the chemical agents and their dilutions are inherently self sterilising, the possibility that they may support the growth of microorganisms or act as a carrier of spores should be taken into account.

Dilutions should be made with water of known microbiological quality (e.g. WFI) using containers and equipment that does not compromise the quality of the disinfectant solution. In some applications aseptic filtration may be appropriate.

3 METHODS FOR TREATING RESIDENT SURFACES

Firstly, it is necessary to remove transient material from the controlled workspace. Where applicable, the internal surfaces should be cleaned with a non-corrosive and low residue detergent. The chosen chemical biocidal surface treatment can then be carried out, the agents rinsed off if necessary, and the surface left dry for the next working session.

Agents often used for these procedures may be divided into sporicidal and nonsporicidal categories.

3.1 Sporicidal agents

These agents have an established ability to kill bacterial endospores and normally all other types of micro-organisms. Examples are chlorine compounds (greater than or equal to 100ppm free chlorine solution), peroxygens such as hydrogen peroxide and peracetic acid, iodine compounds, formaldehyde, glutaraldehyde, and chlorine dioxide.

The effective concentration as a sporicidal agent, the potential risk to operators, and the corrosion effects, should be determined. Isolators venting to the outside may be more suitable for controlling the use and safe disposal or dispersion of these effective but unpleasant chemicals.

3.2 Non-sporicidal Agents

These agents are not sporicidal at the concentrations and contact times normally used. They include lower concentrations of all the sporicidal agents above, as well as the alcohols, phenols, quaternary ammonium compounds, acid anionic and amphoteric surfactants, and chlorhexidine. Other less common nitrogen compounds may also be used.

The person responsible for microbiology should identify the population of micro-organisms to be targeted and select the treatment regime. At lower solution concentrations the possibility of resistant organisms being encountered or developed should be considered. This is more likely to occur with phenols and quaternary ammonium compounds. The use of chlorine compounds reduces this risk, but appropriate management of the system, including rinse and dry procedures on treated surfaces and avoiding the storage of dilute solutions, will provide better control.

The physical removal of micro-organisms by surfactants in aqueous solution followed by subsequent drying can contribute as much control as the use of biocides. Both effective cleaning, and use of biocidal agents should be used in standard control measures.

4 METHODS FOR TREATING TRANSIENT SURFACES

The surfaces of components and aids to preparation (syringes etc.) are usually treated using rapid drying agents, such as alcohol (70% w/v ethanol or isopropanol).

Alcoholic solutions are most effective when mixed with water to give a 60–80% w/v concentration. These alcoholic solutions are not capable of killing bacterial endospores in the contact time normally used therefore it is necessary to reduce the risk of spores being present on the surface treated. The addition of mineral acid or hydrogen peroxide to alcoholic solutions will improve the sporicidal activity.

The solution preparation procedure and its containers should be designed to reduce the risk of solution contaminated with spores being introduced into the controlled work-space of the isolator during the transfer procedure. Since the solutions are not sporicidal it is important to take all reasonable steps to avoid transporting spores on component surfaces into the controlled work space.

Storage areas and handling of sterile components should be properly controlled in order to prevent damage to the packaging materials, which may allow ingress of bacterial spores.

The alcohol treatment itself can be optimised by intelligent design of the sequence of operations. For example, avoid wiping an injection site with a swab that has previously been used to clean the bottom of a vial. The physical action of wiping with a swab is a valuable way of removing micro-organisms by physically enmeshing them in the fibres of the swab.

From the above considerations it can be seen that the efficacy of alcohol treatment depends as much on the surrounding storage, handling, type of treatment selected and sequence of operations as on the selection of alcohol as an agent.

Where components are not damaged by immersion in fluid, the use of 'dunking' tanks containing a suitable biocide is an alternative to the use of alcohol.

5 CONCLUSION

As long as the above procedures are selected with due regard to the actual risks presented by the surrounding environment and these risks are managed, the nonabsolute nature of isolator internal surface treatment and treatment of transient materials can help minimise the number of micro-organisms in the critical work zone.

APPENDIX 7 • GAS STERILIZATION OF ISOLATOR SYSTEMS

SCOPE

This appendix gives details of procedures involving gaseous agents introduced into the controlled work space of the isolator system to sanitise the entire space, integral surfaces and transient or resident components inside. It reduces the numbers of viable micro-organisms to a pre-determined and acceptable level.

1 INTRODUCTION

Alcohol-based solutions are routinely used to sanitize equipment and component surfaces during aseptic processing. The major disadvantage of this technique is that alcoholic agents possess negligible activity against bacterial endospores. Control measures can minimise the incidence of spores on the surfaces of vials, syringe wraps etc., but their absence is not assured. A properly designed and validated gas treatment of isolator systems can reduce the probability of spores surviving and increase the sterility assurance of the product.

2 OBJECTIVES OF GAS STERILIZATION

Various gaseous agents can be used within suitably-designed isolators to achieve sterilization of working and component surfaces, thereby significantly reducing the overall probability of sterility failure in the final product. It must be emphasised that this process is not a method of guaranteeing product sterility, but merely eliminates one of the factors which can result in product contamination during aseptic processing.

3 CHOICE OF AGENT

The ideal sterilant would have the following properties:

- rapidly lethal against all micro-organisms
- highly penetrative
- non-aggressive to metals or polymers
- rapid elimination of residues
- harmless to humans

The agents listed below are generally recognised to be effective biocides, but each has specific disadvantages:

Ethylene oxide is potentially explosive and requires lengthy purge times to eliminate toxic residues. It is toxic and carcinogenic and is absorbed by polymeric materials.

Formaldehyde vapour is noxious, toxic and readily permeates a number of polymers, which may result in chemical contamination of products.

Peracetic acid vapour is rapidly sporicidal and potentially corrosive. It permeates polymers comparatively slowly and degradation products are relatively harmless.

Hydrogen peroxide vapour has similar characteristics to peracetic acid.

The agent of choice will be determined by a number of process and equipment-related factors, but for pharmaceutical applications in isolators the sterilants in most general use are peracetic acid and hydrogen peroxide.

4 FACTORS LEADING TO STERILIZATION FAILURE

As with any antimicrobial agent, gas sterilants are only effective if they are in intimate contact with contaminating organisms at sufficient concentration, and for an adequate period of time. Any physical debris or residues must be cleaned from working or component surfaces before sterilization commences, and all surfaces must be completely dry. The vapour concentration, humidity and contact times are normally controlled by instrumentation on the gas generator (see later).

The most likely cause of microorganisms surviving is through the inability of the sterilant to contact every surface of equipment, components and the isolator's working chamber. Minimal occlusion, such as a glove/sleeve or a syringe pack resting on a worktop may be sufficient to reduce lethality, whilst more flexible items offer greater protection to organisms trapped beneath or between them. It is therefore essential that the loading pattern for the isolator is validated during process development, and is rigorously controlled by operational procedures.

5 VALIDATION OF PROCESS CONDITIONS

5.1 Humidity

When humidity is a significant parameter in the process, steps should be taken to ensure the necessary level is maintained. Excessive humidity may result in condensation and subsequent contamination of the components.

5.2 Air Flow Patterns

Smoke can be used to visualize gas flow within the isolator chamber, allowing patterns for equipment and components to be developed which do not result in obvious areas of low flow. Patterns of gas flow may also be visualised with pH papers if peracetic acid is used.

5.3 Gas Contact

To ensure their effectiveness, the sterilant vapours must be in contact with all contaminated surfaces. The following points should be considered:

- Equipment should be raised appreciably above worktops, and efforts made to provide point contact of supports.
- Components should not be laid on worktops or other solid surfaces. Wire baskets or racking can be utilised to approximate point contact support. Wherever possible, containers and components should be suspended from point contacts (eg wire hooks), to allow free circulation of sterilant around all items. If necessary components should be rotated or repositioned during processing to ensure all surfaces are exposed to the gaseous sterilant.
- Glove/gauntlet fingers should be fully extended, and supported well clear of the worktop in such a way that the glove/sleeve materials are not unduly folded.

6 MICROBIOLOGICAL VALIDATION

Biological indicators (BI) can be used to confirm the effectiveness of the selected conditions and standard loading patterns. The test organisms should be selected to represent a known challenge to the process. In practice, *Bacillus subtilis (var niger)* is frequently used, at a concentration of 10^6 - 10^7 spores per strip. The manufacturers certificate of the D value or a determination of the D value under the actual condition of use provides a reference point to enable the lethality to the natural bio-burden to be estimated.

Initial tests should concentrate on establishing approximate death curves for the test organism, and/or progressively increasing sterilant contact time until the target lethality is achieved. The process contact time and sterilant vapour concentration should then be selected to include an acceptable safety margin, which makes allowance also for the compatibility of equipment and components with the sterilant, and the need to purge residuals before aseptic processing commences. Once process conditions have been established, the cycle/loading pattern should be validated by performing replicate cycles, again using BI's in worst case positions. Positive controls should be performed and the recovery conditions verified. When some degree of occlusion is unavoidable such that the diffusion path of gas is greater than 1 or 2mm, the actual lethality delivered can be investigated by direct innoculation of the surfaces and estimation of survivors. Positive controls should be used for both techniques and recovery conditions verified as being effective.

7 ELIMINATION OF RESIDUALS

In order to minimise the risk of chemical contamination of final product, the sterilant contact time should be as short as possible (subject to effective and reliable sterilization) and the purge time as long as possible (subject to operational constraints). Polymeric containers and various types of disposables packing will allow varying degrees of sterilant permeation, and validation studies should demonstrate that 'worst case' situation will not result in chemical contamination of components or solutions in plastic packaging or containers.

8 ROUTINE CYCLE MONITORING

The correct loading of the isolator prior to gassing should be the subject of properly documented control, and it is good practice for isolator access doors to be locked once correct loading has been checked. The gas generator's airflow and sterilant dispenser flow are often pre-set by the manufacturer, but if this is not the case their correct adjustment should also be formally documented. The generator should ideally allow these parameters, as well as sterilant injection time, to be recorded for each cycle, as happens with steam sterilisers. If the generator does not feature computer or chart recording of data, the parameters should be manually recorded at regular intervals, and documented for each cycle.

9 CONCLUSION

Provided that process conditions are thoroughly validated and working practices are properly controlled, gas sterilization within suitable isolators will consistently eliminate viable micro-organisms including spores on working or component surfaces, thereby contributing to improved reliability in aseptic processing.

Printed in the United Kingdom for HMSO
Dd300080 1/95 C15 G559 10170

Dear Reader

The UK Isolator Group intends to review and update this document in order to ensure that it reflects current practice. To this end, comments and suggestions from those people who use this document would be welcomed.

You may wish to photocopy and submit the pro-forma below or present more detailed written comments.

Correspondence should be addressed to the Chairman of the U.K Isolator Group Mr Brian Midcalf.

Document title: **A SPECIFICATION FOR ISOLATORS FOR PHARMACEUTICAL USES**

Document number ISBN 0 11 701829 5

1. Name:

2. Organisation:

3. Type of organisation: ☐ Vendor ☐ User ☐ Manufacturer

   ☐ Other (specify) ____________________

4. Address: (street, city, state or province, postal code, country)

   ____

   ____

5. Telephone number: ____________ 6. Date of submission: ____________

   ____

7. Proposed areas of change:
   a. Current paragraph number and wording:
   b. Recommended wording
   c. Reason or rationale for recommendation

8. Remarks/comments:

(Additional pages may be attached)